NINJA
ADVENTURES

Editors Beth Davies, Hannah Dolan, Emma Grange, Akansha Jain,
Himani Khatreja, Rosie Peet, Victoria Taylor
Designers Sam Bartlett, David McDonald, James McKeag, Mark Penfound
Thelma-Jane Robb, Gema Salamanca, Rhys Thomas
Senior Pre-production Producer Jennifer Murray
Senior Producer Mandy Inness
Project Manager Clare Millar
Managing Editors Sarah Harland, Paula Regan
Design Managers Jo Connor, Vicky Short
Publisher Julie Ferris
Art Director Lisa Lanzarini
Publishing Director Mark Searle

Reading Consultant Linda B. Gambrell, Ph.D

First American Edition, 2020
Published in the United States by DK Publishing
1450 Broadway, Suite 801, New York, New York 10018
DK, a Division of Penguin Random House LLC

Page design copyright © 2020 Dorling Kindersley Limited

001–320417–March/2020

Contains content previously published in:
LEGO® NINJAGO® *Ninja, Go!* (2015),
LEGO® NINJAGO® *Ninja in Action* (2018),
LEGO® NINJAGO® *The Great Ninja Chase* (2018),
and LEGO® NINJAGO® *How to be a Ninja* (2020)

A catalog record for this book is available from the Library of Congress.

ISBN: 978-0-7440-2176-9

Printed and bound in China

www.dk.com
www.LEGO.com

A WORLD OF IDEAS:
SEE ALL THERE IS TO KNOW

Contents

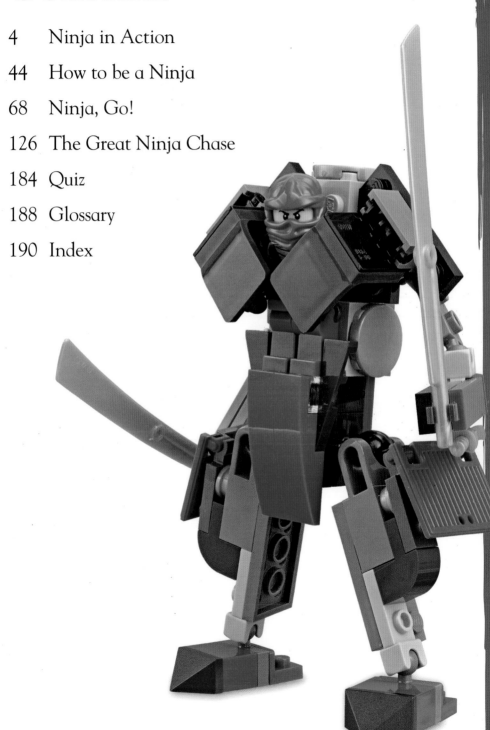

NINJA
IN ACTION

Written by Beth Davies

The ninja

These six ninja
are brave heroes.
They work together
to protect their home,
Ninjago City.

Master Wu is their
wise teacher. He helps
them to train and be the
best ninja they can be.

Lloyd

Jay

Nya

Zane

Cole

Master Wu

Kai

Ninja training

The ninja practice their skills often. Master Wu makes sure they don't forget the skills they have learned. They have a training session with Wu every week.

The ninja practice fighting with different weapons to make sure they are always ready for battle. Master Wu takes photos of the team so they can see their progress.

Lloyd

Lloyd is the Green Ninja.
Lloyd's father is the ninja's
great enemy, Lord Garmadon.

Lloyd is going to be the team's
Master in Training. This is a very
important job. He is always keen
to take on new challenges and
learn new things.

Kai and Nya

Kai and Nya are sister and brother.
Kai is the Ninja of Fire and Nya is
the Ninja of Water. Together they
can win any battle!

Kai is short-tempered and a fierce
fighter. Nya can be sensitive but
she is also tough. They both always
try to be better ninja.

Cole

Cole is a calm and
confident ninja.
He always knows what
to do in a crisis.

Cole is happiest when
practicing his skills
outdoors. He trains all the
time and pushes himself to
be the best that he can be.

Zane

Zane is the oldest of the ninja and he is very clever. He is a bit different from the other ninja. Zane is a type of robot called a Nindroid and he has a control panel in his chest. He was the first Nindroid to be built.

Jay

Jay is a keen and energetic ninja. He likes to tell jokes and make his friends laugh.

Jay's special power is lightning and he has a blade that makes lightning bolts.

Master Wu

Master Wu is very old and very wise. He always helps the ninja to improve their skills. He is quite strict but he can also have fun.

Master Wu loves tea. He even
has his own tea shop. Wu enjoys
sharing a cup of tea and a chat
with Cole after a training session.
It is a good way to relax.

Powers and weapons

The ninja all have different powers
and weapons. This means that
when they work together, they
are able to defeat any enemy.

Lloyd
Power: Energy
Weapon: Katana sword

Jay
Power: Lightning
Weapon: Nunchucks

Kai

Power: Fire
Weapon: Sword of fire

Zane

Power: Ice
Weapon: Shurikens

Cole

Power: Earth
Weapon: Scythe

Nya

Power: Water
Weapon: Sai

Up in the air

Lloyd has a flying vehicle.
It is called *Destiny's Shadow*.
It can also float on water.

Master Wu puts on his helmet
and flies in his hot-air balloon.
Cole flies a plane that can fire
missiles at top speed.

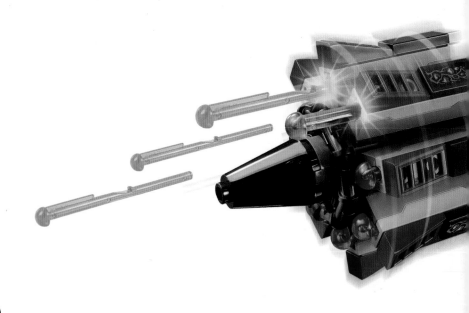

Bike chase

The ninja sometimes ride very fast motorbikes. They are ready to catch even the speediest enemies. Kai and Nya race each other.

Jay is the Lightning Ninja. He is as quick as a flash on his bright blue bike. It can fire missiles at enemies.

On the road

Ninja need powerful vehicles for their battles. Zane's white vehicle has strong armor all over so he is protected inside.

Cole's car has very big wheels, so it is good for racing across bumpy land. When the car stops, Cole jumps out and leaps into action. He is always ready for battle.

Mech battles

Mechs are special vehicles that look like giant robots. The mechs have many weapons and gadgets. The ninja stand inside the mechs to control them.

Can you see Jay and Zane in their mechs? Their mechs are helping them defeat the Anachondrai.

Samurai X

The ninja are not the only heroes in Ninjago City. Samurai X is a brave warrior. Nya has built Samurai X, a special vehicle that has big wheels so it can drive in swamps. Now the heroes can work together!

Cave base

Some of the ninja's vehicles are stored in a big cave. The ninja must keep them safe!

Cave door

Cole's motorbike

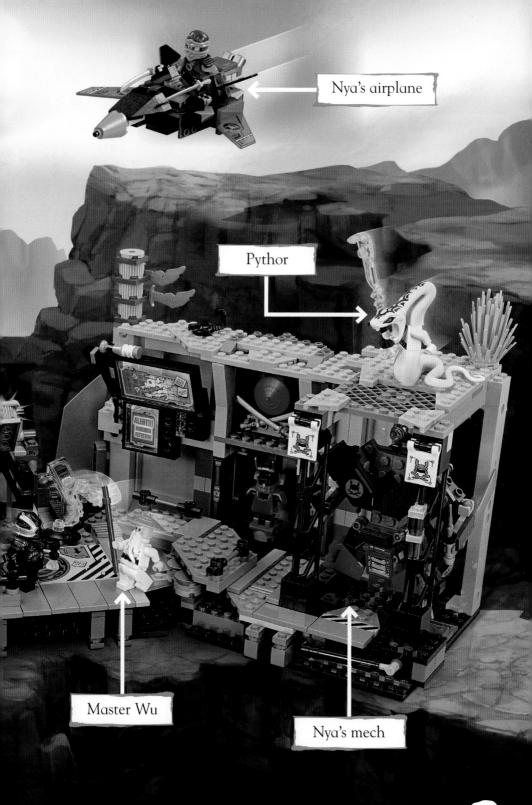

Nya's airplane

Pythor

Master Wu

Nya's mech

The Vermillion

All the ninja's enemies drive strange vehicles. The Vermillion are an army of snakes. They have many strange vehicles including this bike that can drive through swamps.

Sky Pirates

The Sky Pirates are a group
of warriors from a magical place
called Djinjago. The pirates travel
the skies in big ships. They fly
a pirate flag on their ships.

Ghost Army

The Ghost Warriors are spooky villains. They have dragons that they use in battle. Morro is one of the most dangerous Ghost Warriors and he rides a fierce dragon.

Anacondrai

The Anacondrai live in the jungle
and their vehicles are decorated
with bones and skeletons. This
Condrai Copter is very fast.

Ninja battles

The ninja must always be ready to do battle on the ground and in the air. Here the ninja are battling with their enemies the Sky Pirates.

The ninja must work together.
They use their weapons, vehicles,
and fighting skills to defeat the
Sky Pirates. Working together
is always the best plan of action!

Temple of Airjitzu

This temple is the perfect place for the ninja to train and relax. It is surrounded by ancient village shops.

Blacksmith's shop

Postman

Temple of Airjitzu

Zane's glider

Smugglers' market

Statue of Master Yang

43

HOW TO BE
A NINJA

Written by Rosie Peet

Ninja training

In the land of Ninjago live six ninja. These brave warriors keep the land safe. Their names are Nya, Jay, Cole, Lloyd, Kai, and Zane.

Jay

Master Wu

Nya

The ninja's teacher is Master Wu.
He trains the ninja to be skilled
fighters. He doesn't like laziness!

Cole

Kai

Lloyd

Zane

The ninja train hard. They learn how to use cool weapons.

Nya is learning how to use a trident. It has three prongs. It has a dragon on the handle.

The ninja also train in the art of Spinjitzu. They spin really fast to create a tornado of energy. These tornados make them powerful in their battles.

Cole is practicing Spinjitzu. He has created a tornado of fire!

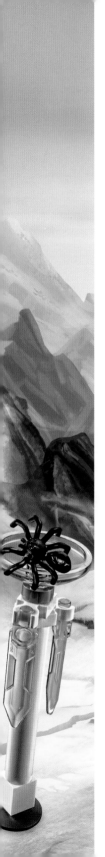

Master Wu has set up a training challenge for Lloyd. Lloyd must use Spinjitzu to grab a sword from a high platform.

Lloyd must be careful. If he lands on the wrong platform, he will meet a creepy spider!

A ninja must be agile as well as
fast. Master Wu has created
an obstacle course to train Jay.

Jay must dodge the flying missiles.
It is hard to avoid missiles when you
are spinning so fast!

It is time for Zane's training! He must hit the target on the training dummy. He also needs to avoid some flying blades. Zane uses Spinjitzu to dodge the blades and reach the dummy.

Kai puts his training into action! He wants to grab a sword. It is a powerful weapon. He jumps and spins toward it.

An enemy Blizzard Warrior has the same idea! Who will get there first?

Desert duels

The ninja chase enemies in their vehicles. Ninja must be able to travel on land, on water, and in the air.

Master Wu steers his flyer over
the hot desert. Nya follows in a
speedy quad bike.

Wu's flyer and Nya's quad bike fit onto the Land Bounty. The Land Bounty is the ninja's main vehicle. It has sails like a ship. It has six wheels. It can drive over rocky ground.

Main sail

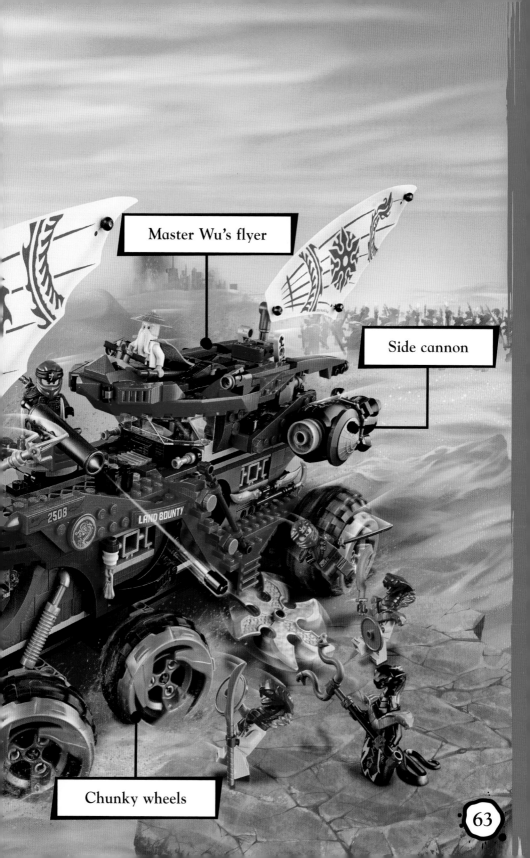

Master Wu's flyer

Side cannon

2508

LAND BOUNTY

Chunky wheels

Cole and Nya are battling under the hot sun. They are fighting the sneaky snakes. Nya uses her Spinjitzu skills to attack Char. Cole rides in on his Dirt Bike to face Pyro Whipper.

Aspheera is a Serpentine with magical powers. She is a fierce enemy. She rides a giant snake called Fire Fang across the desert. Fire Fang has sharp fangs and can breathe fire!

Nya has come face-to-face
with Aspheera and Fire Fang.
Watch out, Nya! Fire Fang
has fiery breath and a
thrashing tail!

Thrashing tail

Swords

Aspheera's throne

Fiery breath

The Never-Realm

Zane is flying his Shuricopter over the icy Never-Realm. He is looking for the Scroll of Forbidden Spinjitzu.

The Shuricopter has two sets of sharp blades at the front. It shoots missiles from two cannons.

Jay is battling an Ice Warrior.
The Ice Warrior has the scroll on
a long sword.

Jay uses his Spinjitzu skills to try to grab the scroll. The Ice Warrior dodges out of the way.

Lloyd is battling a fierce Blizzard Warrior. Lloyd remembers his training. He puts his sword skills into action!

Lloyd's friend Akita can turn into a wolf with three tails. She sneaks up on the icy foe. Lloyd and Akita defeat the Blizzard Warrior together.

Zane and Lloyd are taking on a whole army of Blizzard Warriors! Zane uses his Spinjitzu powers against two enemies. A Blizzard Archer and a Blizzard Sword Master are no match for Lloyd's mighty Titan Mech.

The ninja see something in the
sky. It is the Forbidden Ice Dragon!
This dragon has huge wings, sharp
claws, and a long tail.

The Forsaken Emperor sits on the Dragon's back. He is holding the scroll!

Lloyd, Cole, and Akita follow the dragon to the Castle of the Forsaken Emperor. Blizzard Warriors fire arrows from tall towers.

The Forsaken Emperor sits on a high throne. Lloyd tries to reach him but he gets trapped in icicles! Lloyd uses Spinjitzu to break free.

The Emperor has come down from
his throne. Lloyd battles against
him one-on-one! Lloyd puts his
Spinjitzu training into practice.

Lloyd spins fast and dodges the
Emperor's blade. Lloyd is so fast
that he is able to grab the scroll
from the Emperor!

The ninja drive cool vehicles, use awesome weapons, and spin like tornados. They use their skills to defeat fierce enemies.

The ninja are ready to face anything. Master Wu is proud of his students. Now you know how to be a ninja, too!

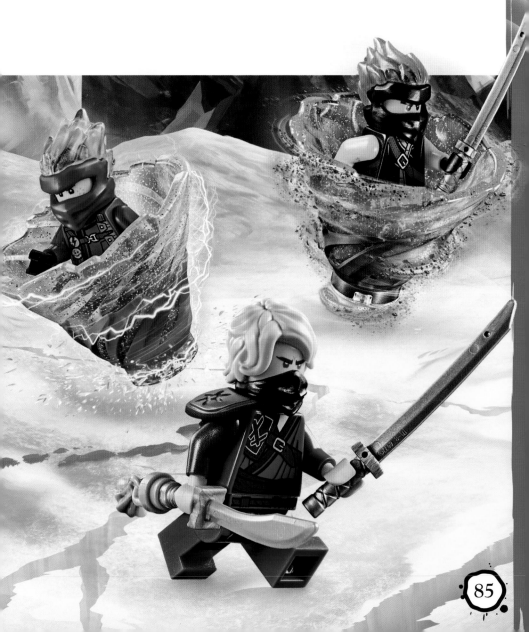

NINJA, GO!

Written by Julia March

World of Ninjago

Five brave ninja protect this magical land. Their names are Cole, Jay, Kai, Zane, and Lloyd.

They are masters of a martial art called Spinjitzu. The ninja possess powers of the four Elements of Ninjago. These are Earth, Lightning, Fire, and Ice.

Ninja, no more

The ninja are sad. Zane
went missing after a battle
with an enemy.

Where could Zane be?
The ninja do not feel
like a team without him,
so they split up.

Kai

This red ninja is
the Master of Fire.
He has a hot temper!
Now that the ninja team
has split up, Kai works
as a show fighter.
He thrills the audience
with his acrobatic moves.

Jay

Skillful Jay is the
Master of Lightning.
This blue ninja is super
fast and adventurous.
Now that the ninja team
has split up, Jay works
as a game show host.
His jokes make the
audience laugh!

Cole

This black ninja is
the Master of Earth.
He is very strong and calm.
Now that the ninja team
has split up, Cole works
as a lumberjack.
Chopping down trees
keeps him busy.

Lloyd Garmadon

This green ninja is the
Master of all Elements.
He is upset that the
team split up.
He does not want to
get another job.
Lloyd still wants to be
a ninja more than anything!

Zane

Zane is the Ninja of Ice.
He is a quiet and serious robot.
The other ninja think that
Zane has been destroyed,
but he has rebuilt himself.
Where has he gone?
Will he ever see
his friends again?

NINJA WEAPONS

JAY

GOLDEN STRIKER

Description: Three-pointed dagger

Use: Sharp jabs in close combat

ZANE

SHURIKENS OF ICE

Description: Throwing stars

Use: Spin towards target with extreme force

COLE

STAFF OF THE DRAGONS

Description: Solid, long stick

Use: Strikes enemy and blocks attacks

KAI

GOLDEN KATANA

Description: Razor-sharp blade

Use: Cuts, slices, and defends enemy attacks

Master Wu

Master Wu is a wise
and good teacher.
He taught the ninja
all of their skills.

Sensei Garmadon

Sensei Garmadon is
Master Wu's brother.
He used to be evil,
but now he is good.

NINJAGO TIMES

Volume 12

SENSEI GARMADON WRITES BOOK

Sensei Garmadon has written a book about his exciting life. We asked him to tell us more!

Can you tell us more about your transformation from bad to good?

I was a wicked dark lord. I told lies and even plotted to take over Ninjago! Now instead of fighting the ninja, I spend my time training them.

 **REMEMBERING ZANE:** New statue for much missed ninja built in town center.

 **MYSTERIOUS POSTERS:** Master Chen's followers put up posters in Ninjago. A special report.

Why did you change?

My son, Lloyd, and my brother, Wu, changed me with their goodness. I owe them my life.

Do you have a message for our readers?

I hope my story inspires other villains to give up their life of crime and live in harmony. Peace out!

IN ALL GOOD BOOKSHOPS!

Sensei Garmadon

An Autobiography

MY JOURNEY FROM EVIL TO GOOD

Master Chen

This villain is Master Chen.
He wants to turn people into
snakes called Anacondrai!
To do this, he must steal the
powers of the ninja. So he
invites them to a contest
on his island.

Master Chen
presents:

THE TOURNAMENT OF ELEMENTS!

Are you the most powerful warrior in Ninjago?

Come to Master Chen's island to prove it!

BE THERE

(Bring this flyer for one free bowl of noodles)

Nya

Nya is Kai's younger sister.
She is very clever.
Nya thinks that the
tournament is a trap!
She follows the ninja
to Master Chen's island.
She hopes she will find
Zane there, too.

TOURNAMENT ARENA

Welcome to Master Chen's tournament arena. The ninja find that it is full of surprise obstacles. Enter at your own risk!

Swerve to sidestep the falling swords.

Dodge spinning blades!

Don't fall down the trapdoor leading to the fire prison!

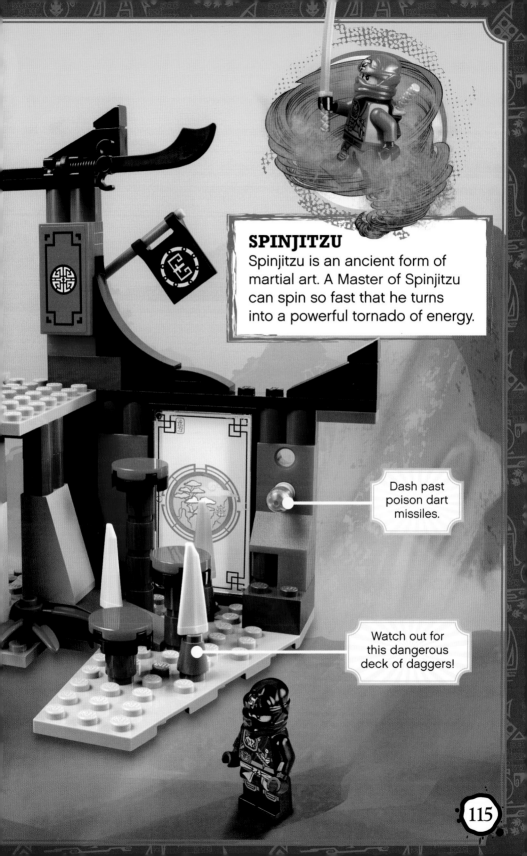

SPINJITZU
Spinjitzu is an ancient form of martial art. A Master of Spinjitzu can spin so fast that he turns into a powerful tornado of energy.

Dash past poison dart missiles.

Watch out for this dangerous deck of daggers!

Skylor

Skylor is Chen's daughter.
She can steal the power
of any ninja she touches.
Chen wants her to steal
the powers of the ninja.
But when she meets Kai,
she wants to be friends
with them instead!

Clouse

Evil Clouse has a Book of Magic.
He uses a magic spell to help
Chen turn people into snakes.
It even works on Garmadon!

Pythor

Pythor has always been a snake.
Master Chen needs his help
to make Clouse's magic spell
last forever.

CHEN'S EVIL PLAN

Master Chen's follower, Eyezor, is devoted but dim. He is still confused about Chen's plan to defeat the ninja and conquer Ninjago.

Anacondrai Army

Master Chen is now the leader
of a huge Anacondrai army!
He thinks nothing can stop
his plan to take over Ninjago.
But Sensei Garmadon still has
a good heart, even as a snake!
He uses a spell from the Book
of Magic to send Chen and
the Anacondrai far away.

Ninja reunion

The Anacondrai are beaten!
Master Chen is gone for good.
But what really makes the ninja
happy is seeing Zane again!

He was a prisoner on Chen's island, but now he is free. All five ninja are back together. Where will their adventures take them next?

THE GREAT
NINJA CHASE

Written by Hannah Dolan

MEET THE NINJA

Let's meet all the friends and foes who will play a part in our exciting story—from brave ninja warriors to slithering snakes. It doesn't matter if you have different friends and foes in your LEGO® NINJAGO® collection. They are all welcome to join in, too!

LLOYD

Lloyd is the Green Ninja. He is the youngest member of the team, but also the most powerful. He loves his new mech!

NYA

Nya is Kai's sister. She has proven herself to be just as brave as her ninja brother and his teammates.

ZANE

As the Ninja of Ice, Zane is always cool under pressure. He is a little different from the other ninja, as he is really a robot!

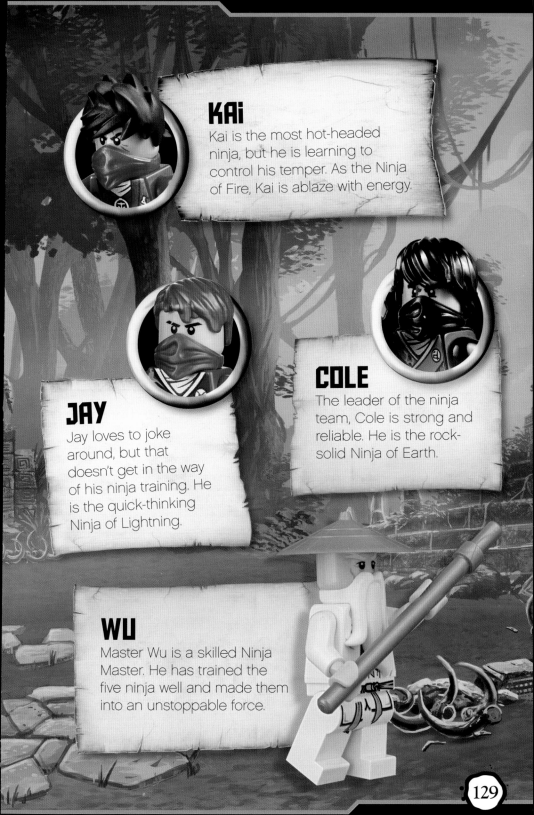

KAI

Kai is the most hot-headed ninja, but he is learning to control his temper. As the Ninja of Fire, Kai is ablaze with energy.

COLE

The leader of the ninja team, Cole is strong and reliable. He is the rock-solid Ninja of Earth.

JAY

Jay loves to joke around, but that doesn't get in the way of his ninja training. He is the quick-thinking Ninja of Lightning.

WU

Master Wu is a skilled Ninja Master. He has trained the five ninja well and made them into an unstoppable force.

Trouble at home

Welcome to the ninja's home! There is space here for all the ninja to hang out. This is the ground floor. It has raised floorboards and wooden beams.

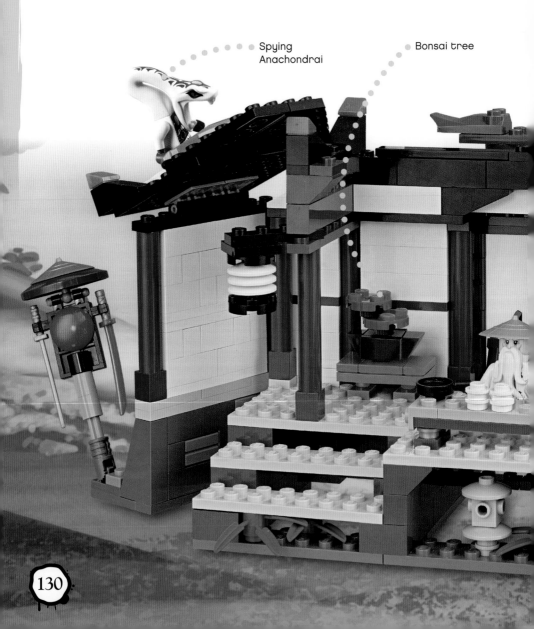

Spying Anachondrai

Bonsai tree

Master Wu and Zane are in the meditation room. They can relax there knowing that the entire house is protected by traps that are designed to catch out any unwelcome visitors.

Decorative wooden doorway

Zane, chilling out

When the ninja need some down time at home, they hang out in their games room. This is where they watch TV, play computer games, and eat pizza. Kai is so busy relaxing, he hasn't noticed that three pairs of eyes are watching him through the window!

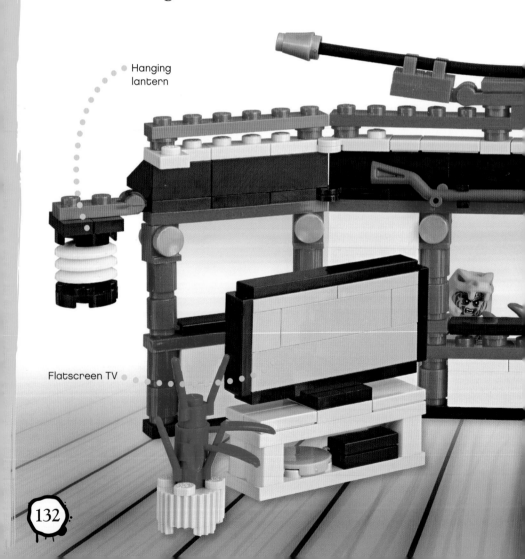

Hanging lantern

Flatscreen TV

The sneaky Anacondrai are spying on the ninja at home because they want to steal their secrets. They had better not make any sudden moves. Kai may have his feet up, but he is always ready for battle. Can you spot his golden dagger hidden at the side of the sofa?

Comfortable armrest

Chain swing

Sturdy towers
support the
swing gym

Cole likes to be super-fit, so he has
built a training course outside the ninja's
house. He powers across a swing gym
and speeds over balance beams. Don't
look down, Cole! The outdoor gym tests
Cole's strength, agility, and reflexes—
everything a ninja needs to fight
his enemies.

Monkey bars

One of the Anacondrai has been sent to spy on Cole. When he sees how strong and skilled Cole is, he quickly slithers away!

Narrow, uneven wooden beams

Nya has a cool workshop in the basement of the house. She has just finished building something—an awesome Green Ninja Mech for Lloyd. He thinks it's the greatest mech ever!

The pair decide to lock away the blueprints for the mech so they can't be stolen by their enemies. But just as Lloyd is printing them out, they are distracted by a sound. They dash off to investigate, leaving the blueprints unattended.

TV aerial

Computer levers and dials

Printer, churning out the blueprints

THE ANACONDRAI

A tribe of sinister snakes and their human henchmen, the Anacondrai are known for having the most powerful warriors in NINJAGO City. They are out to cause trouble wherever they can!

PYTHOR

Pythor is a true Anacondrai! His misadventures have left him bleached white, but his devious mind is still full of colorful plans.

CHOP'RAI

The loyal Anacondrai warrior, Chope, has used Pythor's venom to transform into the sly, blade-wielding serpent, Chop'rai.

KAPU'RAI

Like Chope, Kapau achieved his dream and has become the armored snake, Kapu'rai.

CHOPE-CHOPE

Chope-Chope invented his own name to seem menacing—although some would say his scary grimace and ruthless fighting style are enough for that!

KAPAU

Kapau also named himself to sound tough and scary. He is rising quickly through the ranks of the army!

SLEVEN

Sleven is more than willing to take on Anacondrai powers. This slithery guy already acts like a snake, he now just needs a tail!

Jay relaxing
in the bath •••••••

Rubber duck ••••••

House of Ninja

The Anacondrai have stolen
the plans for the Green Ninja Mech!
They distracted Lloyd and Nya, then
seized their chance while the other ninja
relaxed. Jay rushes from the bathroom
and joins the others just in time to see
the snakes slithering away. The ninja
agree that they must get the plans back,
 no matter what!

Chasing the
Anacondrai

There's room inside for all the ninja

Jungle battle

The ninja are in pursuit of the sneaky Anacondrai who have stolen their Green Ninja Mech blueprints. Jay thinks the snakes will head for the jungle, so the ninja pack up all the equipment they will need and make their way into the wild...

Fallen pillar • • • • • •

The ninja will need a place to sleep in the jungle, so Jay has built a tent for the trip. He sets up camp near the crumbling ruins of an old temple. It has become overgrown with jungle trees and plants. The ninja can hide here unnoticed by the Anachondrai.

The old temple doorway

Crooked tree, growing out of the ruins

Push here and the
plant snaps shut!

Jay was right: the Anacondrai
are in the jungle! Cole spots one
of their henchmen on patrol in a
powerful hovercraft. Jay is quick
to give chase in his super-fast
speeder, but this steamy swamp
is not an easy place to navigate.
Can Jay catch him?

Jay skims over the swamp at high speed but he needs to look out. Things are not what they seem in the jungle. The Anacondrai have set traps to stop him. That plant up ahead may be about to snap shut like hungry jaws!

Whirring propeller

Flick-fire missile

Blade glides over
swamp water

Jay manages to move further into the swamp, but he finds even more obstacles blocking his way. He decides to park up his speeder and travel on foot. He knows he must use his lightning-fast skills to dodge the traps the Anacondrai have set for him.

Mossy surface

Jay has spotted one of the Anachondrai at the other side of a rickety bamboo bridge. It's covered in slippery moss and underneath it are some spiky-looking lily pads. Jay has to cross it carefully, giving the Anachondrai the chance to slip away!

Broken bamboo beams

Lily pads in the water below

Side blaster

Jay reaches the far side of the swamp, but the slippery Anacondrai are nowhere to be seen. He spots some tire tracks leading off between the trees. It looks like the snakes have a car to help them get away! Lucky that Jay has a mighty 4x4 to carry on the chase...

The huge wheels on Jay's 4x4 take him deep into snake territory. It has a spinning blaster cannon on the front that should rattle any snake! The Anachondrai henchman driving the snake car knows Jay is on his tail, literally! He uses his car's small size to zip through the jungle.

Swishing, bony tail

Snake-head front bumper

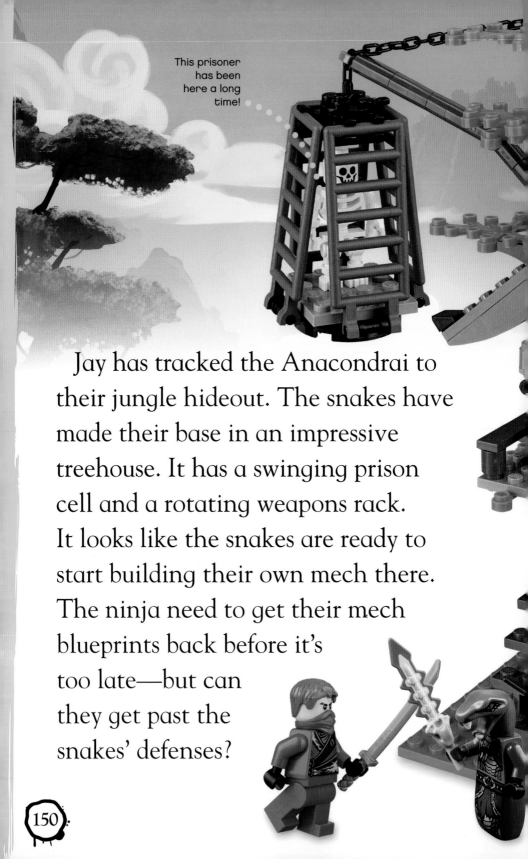

This prisoner has been here a long time!

Jay has tracked the Anacondrai to their jungle hideout. The snakes have made their base in an impressive treehouse. It has a swinging prison cell and a rotating weapons rack. It looks like the snakes are ready to start building their own mech there. The ninja need to get their mech blueprints back before it's too late—but can they get past the snakes' defenses?

Circular treehouse
entrance

Crane for winching
supplies up from
the jungle floor

Weapons rack

151

Going Underground

The Anacondrai got away from the ninja in the jungle, and have slithered away with the stolen blueprints once more. Cole suspects they have gone underground and tracks them to a spooky cave.

The cave was once a busy gold mine, but it has since been abandoned. The ninja don't hesitate to follow the Anachondrai inside. They should be wary—there are all kinds of traps waiting for them in the dark!

Moss covers the top of the entrance

Wild weeds

Dripping snake venom

Deep in the cave, the ninja find some lanterns. When they light them, they see a glinting pair of fangs! Thankfully it's not a giant snake—it's a digging machine. It looks like the Anacondrai are making an underground base. The ninja follow an Anacondrai worker to see where he goes.

Frightening
front fangs

Cog wheels dig
through the earth

Glowing
venom rock

Look out, Cole! He has triggered a
rockfall trap laid by the Anachondrai.
Venomous rocks tumble down on him
as he knocks them aside with his sword.

There is a lot of old mining equipment this far inside the cave. The ninja find tools and rusty mining carts that must have been left there a long time ago when the cave was a busy gold mine.

Rusty patch

It looks as if the ninja have reached a dead end when Jay spots some old explosives and a detonator. Cole blasts through the wall to see what's on the other side...

Sticks of dynamite

Detonator box

On the other side of the cave wall, the ninja are amazed to find a huge cavern filled with treasure. At its center is a giant stone samurai head and the dusty floor is littered with ancient bones.

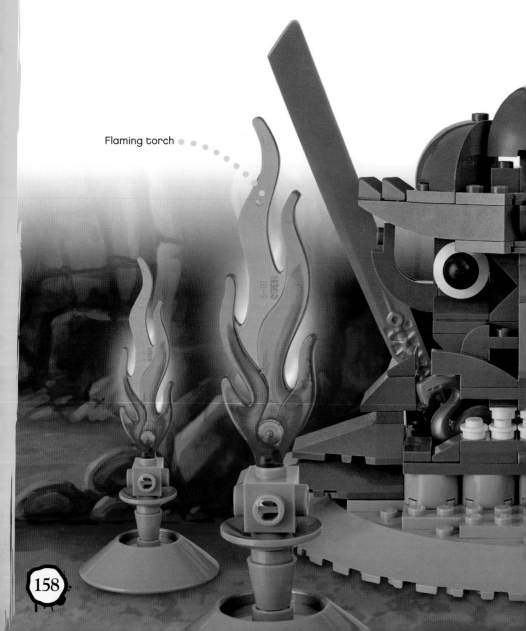

Flaming torch

Lloyd trips on a snake skeleton and reaches out to grab a rock. The rock moves and the samurai head begins to open! The ninja spot a treasure hidden inside its mouth—a shimmering golden sword.

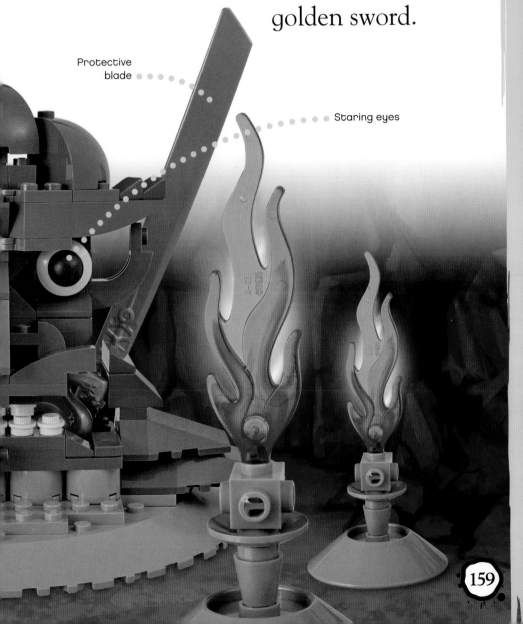

Protective blade

Staring eyes

Saw-toothed
blades

The Anacondrai burst into the cavern eager to get their hands on the treasure that the ninja have found. They haven't come alone, either—they have tamed a huge, rocky snake that lives in these dark depths. Even worse, the mech plans are nowhere to be seen!

Only Cole's saw-mobile can get the ninja out of this. Its monster saw blades are more than a match for the terrifying snake beast's swinging claws.

Fishing rod holds chicken leg bate

Chain to control the creature

Hungry, snapping jaws

Volcano quest

The Anacondrai escaped the caves and slithered away towards a fiery volcano. The ninja give chase, crossing a bridge into a village at the foot of the volcano. Kai and Nya are the first to notice something is wrong. There's no one there!

Shop sign

龍
神
忍者

Flaming, bubbling lava

This abandoned village shop is filled with crates of untouched goods. Did all the villagers run away to escape the relentless lava flow, or was it the Anachondrai who chased them away?

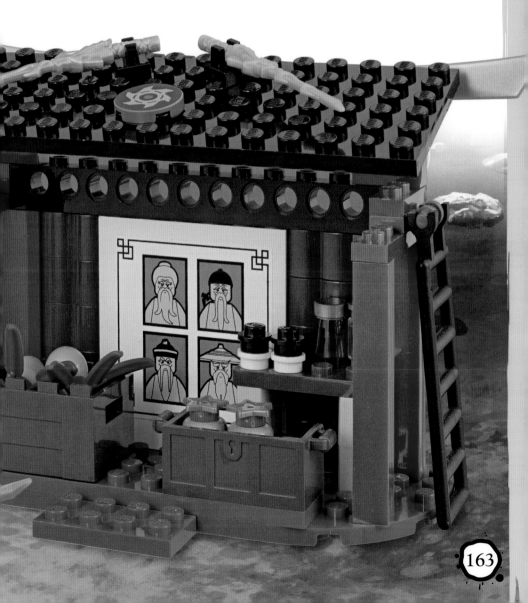

Tail fins help direct the glider

It looks like the ninja have headed in the right direction as they leave the village. There are scary Anacondrai warning signs lining the pathway! The Anachondrai have made them from bones, skulls, horns, and spears to scare away the ninja.

Signs don't frighten the Ninja of Fire! Kai has a blazing fire glider to help him speed his way to the top of the volcano. It has dragon claws for wings and long tail fins. At the front is the symbol of the phoenix—a creature born out of the ashes of fire.

Flapping, clawed wing

Scarred skull

Phoenix bumper symbol

Few people have ever been this high up on the volcano before, so the ninja are surprised to find a grand gateway here. It is surrounded by burning hot rocks. Is it the entrance to another hideout?

Decorative details mark the entrance

Glowing lava rock

There's only one way to find out! The ninja go through, only to see an enormous fire serpent rising up from the fiery lava. The serpent guards this particular route. Run, ninja!

Long, pointed horns

Ferocious head flame

Tall control
tower

Fire pit

Missile, ready
to fire

Beyond the fire serpent, the ninja
find out what it was defending: an
Anacondrai base where the snakes
and their soldiers are making new and
unusual weapons. There's a weapons
forge with a roaring fire for heating up
metal, and a venomous missile launcher.

Anvil for
shaping
weapons

Luckily Kai has a blazing set of wheels
to tear through the base! A weapons
factory won't stop the ninja.

Heatproof
windshield

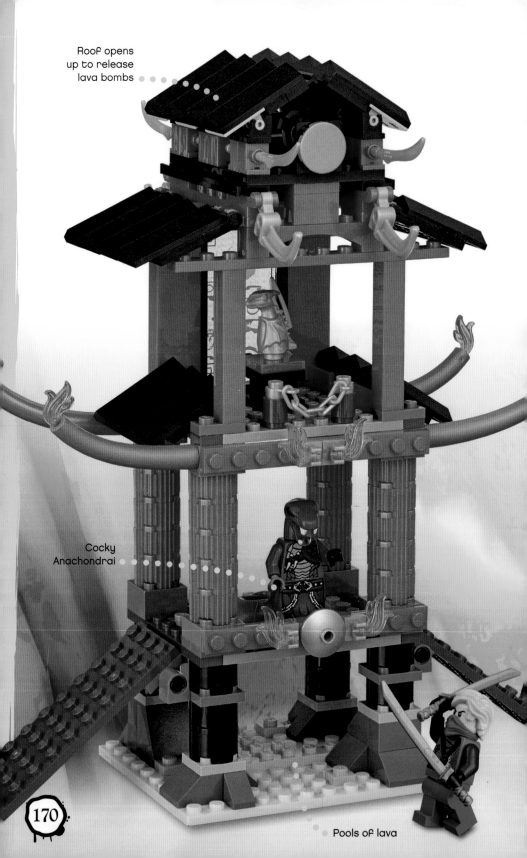

Roof opens
up to release
lava bombs

Cocky
Anachondrai

Pools of lava

At the very top of the volcano, the ninja discover an ancient temple that towers above the bubbling lava. The Anacondrai have made this their new base for building their mech—and they are very nearly finished! The Anachondrai have also built a fiery surprise in the temple's roof—it's filled with lava bombs! They blast the ninja with them and escape once more. Things are really hotting up now!

The Big Freeze

The ninja have come a long way since the Anacondrai stole their mech blueprints. Now they have traced their enemies to the freezing mountains. Everything here is covered in a thick layer of snow and ice—and is very, very slippery! Surely this must be the setting for their final showdown?

Block of ice

Unfortunate explorer

Hanging icicles

Water fountain from a hot spring below ground

Icy slope

It is not easy struggling through the snow and ice on foot. Zane has a powerful ice glider to speed across the frozen landscape. He is searching for the Anachondrai in it when they launch an ice-cold attack in a snowmobile.

Chilly Anachondrai henchman

Blade-like skis

Hidden cannon

The Anachondrai should know better than to challenge the Ninja of Ice! Zane keeps a cool head. His glider's cannons, swords, and pincers can defend a snake attack from all sides.

Protective rear blades

Ice crystals

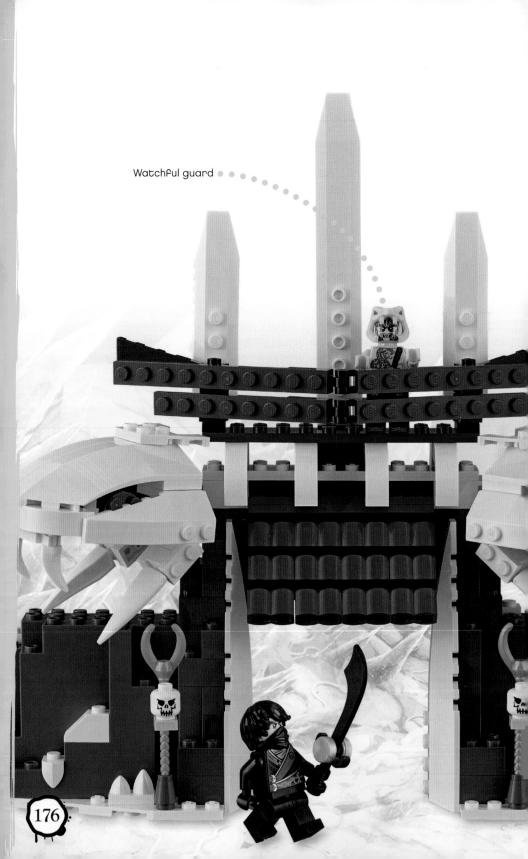

Watchful guard

As the ninja make their way up into the mountains, they spot two enormous, snapping snake skulls on the horizon. They're watching over the entrance to a frightening frozen fortress that can only be the Anacondrai's icy base. It looks like the snakes don't want any visitors. Do the ninja dare go in? They have no choice if they want their mech plans back!

Purple eyes

Blade defenses

The entrance to the fortress is too heavily guarded to simply walk right in. So Zane uses his ice helicopter to look at the fortress from above and spots a second, secret door. The five ninja sneak in, only to find the Anacondrai are already waiting for them!

Bones add a scary touch

Weapons rack

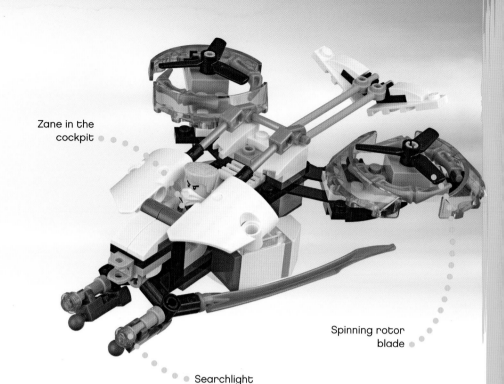

Zane in the
cockpit

Spinning rotor
blade

Searchlight

The snakes have created
a special outdoor arena
for a mech-on-mech
battle. "Welcome to the
war of the mechsss,"
they hiss.

Snowy arena
floor

The Anacondrai have completed their mech just in time for the ninja's arrival. Now the ninja can see what they're up against. Lloyd is ready in his Green Ninja mech.

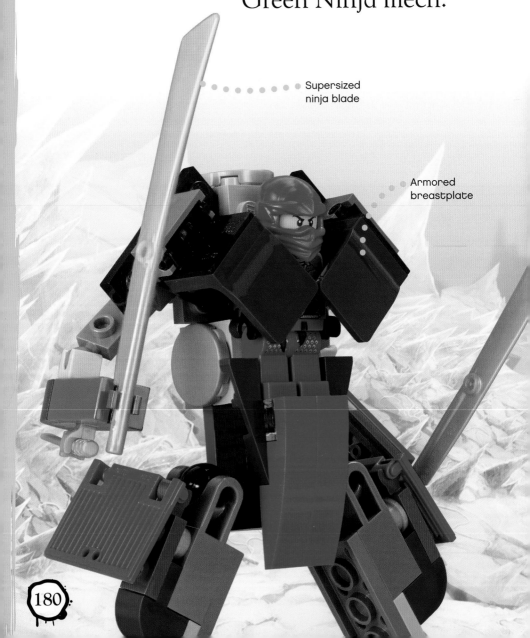

Supersized
ninja blade

Armored
breastplate

The ninja's enemies haven't just copied the stolen mech plans—they have added a whole new, snake-like spin to them. Their mech has the head and body of a serpent! The battle is on, and there can be only one winner.

Fanged head

Steering
control

It's a tough battle when mech meets mech, but it's soon clear that Lloyd has the upper hand. His Green Ninja Mech easily stands up to the snake mech's arm blaster bolts—and his dual swords are

Leg shield

Stomping feet

more than a match for the sharpest fangs. As the defeated Anacondrai mech slinks away, the ninja agree never to leave their secret plans lying around again!

Victorious ninja

Quiz

1. Which ninja are brother and sister?

2. Who is the Ninja of Earth?

3. What is Jay's weapon of choice?

4. What is the name of Lloyd's flying vehicle?

5. Who is the ninja's teacher?

6. What is the name of the ninja's main vehicle?

7. Which ninja has a Dirt Bike?

8. Which power lets the ninja spin like tornados?

9. What is the name of Aspheera's giant snake?

10. True or false? Akita can turn into a polar bear with three tails.

11. What kind of flying animal does the Emperor ride?

12. What does Lloyd get stuck in at the Castle of the Forsaken Emperor?

13. Where do the ninja live?

Quiz (Continued)

14. Which martial art have the ninja mastered?

15. What does Kai work as after the ninja split up?

16. Where is Master Chen holding the Tournament of Elements?

17. What is Zane's element?

18. What power does Skylor have?

19. Who is Lloyd's father?

20. Is Zane the Ninja of Ice or the Ninja of Fire?

21. Who is the youngest ninja?

22. Where does Jay set up the ninja's camp?

23. Who steals the Green Ninja Mech blueprints while the ninja are distracted?

24. The ninja follow the Anacondrai into an abandoned gold mine. True or False?

25. What does the samurai head have hidden inside its mouth?

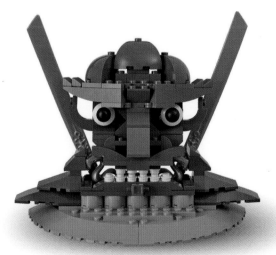

Answers on page 191

Glossary

abandoned
Having been deserted or left

acrobatic
Quick and flexible

agility
Ability to move quickly and easily

ancient
Very old

armor
Strong layer to protect a person or vehicle

autobiography
Book written by a person on the subject of his or her life

bamboo
A giant, woody grass

cannon
A large, heavy gun

convert
To change something

cavern
A large cave

detonator
A device used to make something explode

foe
Enemy

forsaken
Abandoned or left alone

gadgets
A small mechanic or electric tool

henchman
A sidekick or helper

martial art
A form of fighting or self-defense

meditation
The practice of clearing or focusing the mind

missiles
Objects that are thrown or fired

navigate
To plan and direct the course of a ship, aircraft or other form of transport

obstacle
An object that blocks one's way

obstacle course
A series of challenges to test someone's strength and agility

quad bike
A motorbike with four wheels

reflex
Something that you do automatically without thinking

reunion
Meeting up with a person or people after being separated for a period of time

robot
A machine that resembles a living creature

rickety
In bad condition and therefore likely to break

skillful
Having the ability to do something well

tornado
Strong winds that whirl in a spiral

tournament
A series of contests between a number of competitors

trident
A type of weapon that has three prongs

vehicle
Used for moving people or goods

venomous
A poisonous animal or plant

warrior
Someone who fights in battles

Index

Answers to the quiz on page 184–187

1. Kai and Nya 2. Cole 3. Nunchucks 4. *Destiny's Shadow* 5. Master Wu 6. The Land Bounty 7. Cole 8. Spinjitzu 9. Fire Fang 10. False. She can turn into a wolf with three tails. 11. A dragon 12. Icicles 13. Ninjago City 14. Spinjitzu 15. Show fighter 16. On his island 17. Ice 18. She can steal the ninja's power 19. Sensei Garmadon 20. Ninja of Ice 21. Lloyd 22. Near the crumbling ruins of an old temple 23. The Anacondrai 24. True 25. A shimmering golden sword

A LEVEL FOR EVERY READER

This book is a part of an exciting four-level reading series to support children in developing the habit of reading widely for both pleasure and information. Each book is designed to develop a child's reading skills, fluency, grammar awareness, and comprehension in order to build confidence and enjoyment when reading.

Ready for a Level 2 (Beginning to Read) book

A child should:

- be able to recognize a bank of common words quickly and be able to blend sounds together to make some words.
- be familiar with using beginner letter sounds and context clues to figure out unfamiliar words.
- sometimes correct his/her reading if it doesn't look right or make sense.
- be aware of the need for a slight pause at commas and a longer one at periods.

A valuable and shared reading experience

For many children, reading requires much effort, but adult participation can make reading both fun and easier. Here are a few tips on how to use this book with a young reader:

Check out the contents together:

- read about the book on the back cover and talk about the contents page to help heighten interest and expectation.
- discuss new or difficult words.
- chat about labels, annotations, and pictures.

Support the reader:

- give the book to the young reader to turn the pages.
- where necessary, encourage longer words to be broken into syllables, sound out each one, and then flow the syllables together; ask him/her to reread the sentence to check the meaning.
- encourage the reader to vary her/his voice as she/he reads; demonstrate how to do this if helpful.

Talk at the end of each book, or after every few pages:

- ask questions about the text and the meaning of the words used—this helps develop comprehension skills.
- read the quiz at the end of the book and encourage the reader to answer the questions, if necessary, by turning back to the relevant pages to find the answers.

Series consultant, Dr. Linda Gambrell, Distinguished Professor of Education at Clemson University, has served as President of the National Reading Conference, the College Reading Association, and the International Reading Association.